Introduction and background

1. Hospital catering is an essential part of patient care. Patients need nutritious, appetising food that they are able to eat to aid their recovery. Each year the NHS in England and Wales spends about £275 million on hospital catering and produces approximately 220 million meals.[I] Seventy-one per cent of trusts have in-house catering departments, the remainder have contracted out catering services.

2. The separate NHS Plans for England and Wales have raised the profile of hospital catering.[II] [III] They both set out agendas for providing 'Better Hospital Food' by improving the range of meals available for patients, the quality of the food and its nutritional content. In May 2001 a national NHS menu designed by leading chefs was introduced in England and trusts must now give patients access to a 24-hour catering service. The agenda for catering services now rightly includes quality and nutrition as well as cost.

3. Patients' food is not the only concern of hospital catering services. Providing a service for patients may account for less than half of a catering department's activity, most hospitals also provide food for staff and visitors and raise revenue in this way [BOX A]. This review covers both patient and non-patient services. It also considers the roles of dietitians, nurses, porters, housekeepers and support staff in delivering the catering service.

Box A

Services provided by a catering department

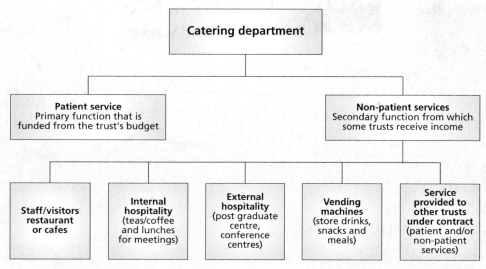

I   Audit Commission. May 2000. Survey of Trusts Providing Acute Services.

II   Department of Health. July 2000. *NHS Plan*. Further details can be found on the web site www.betterhospitalfood.com

III   National Assembly for Wales. January 2001. *Improving Health in Wales*.

4. This review reports the national results of an investigation of hospital catering carried out recently by the Audit Commission as part of its Acute Hospital Portfolio (see back cover). It is based on data for 1999/2000. Almost all NHS hospitals in England and Wales were involved, as were the external contractors who provide services to some trusts. Comparative data were collected and used by auditors to produce a tailored performance assessment for each NHS trust and recommend any necessary further audit work.

5. The main sections of this review consider:

- patients' nutritional needs and how these are identified and met;
- quality of the service provided and the relationship between quality and costs;
- expenditure on catering and the variation between trusts;
- the management and control of costs; and
- potential savings available from reducing food wastage on wards.

Findings

...up to 40 per cent of adults are either admitted to hospital with malnutrition or become malnourished during their stay

Patients' nutritional needs

6. The key aim of any hospital catering service is to provide nutritious meals that meet patients' needs and aid their recovery. There are two aspects to this:

- Correctly identifying their needs.
- Fulfilling their needs through the meals served.

Identifying patients' nutritional needs

7. In recent years there has been increasing concern about the high prevalence of malnutrition among hospital patients.[I] Studies show that up to 40 per cent of adults are either admitted to hospital with malnutrition or become malnourished during their stay.[II III] It is important that trusts identify at-risk patients when they are admitted so that they receive the appropriate level of care. Dietitians play an important role in training nurses to undertake the nutritional screening and in developing a protocol.

[I]   Malnutrition refers to the wasting condition that results from a deficiency of energy (calories) and protein and is accompanied by varying degrees of trace nutrient (vitamin and mineral) deficiencies.

[II]   British Association for Parenteral and Enteral Nutrition. 1999. *Hospital Food as Treatment*.

[III]   The Nuffield Trust. 1999. *Managing Nutrition in Hospital: A Recipe for Quality*.

In 41 per cent of trusts, the dietitians responded that they were unable to see all referred patients.

8. The Audit Commission survey showed that 77 per cent of trusts have a nutritional screening protocol in place that is carried out by nurses. However, less than half of these trusts review patients' nutrition weekly to ensure that care is adjusted to their changing needs during their stay in hospital. It is not clear how patients' nutritional needs are routinely identified in the remaining 23 per cent of trusts.

9. The most serious cases of potential malnutrition and patients with special dietary needs will be referred to the dietitian for a detailed assessment and prescription of an appropriate diet. In 41 per cent of trusts, the dietitians responded that they were unable to see all referred patients. These trusts therefore need to review their policies to ensure that they can identify and respond to the nutritional needs of their most vulnerable patients.

Fulfilling patients' nutritional needs

10. Dietitians also have a role in ensuring appropriate nutritional content and quality of food. By engaging with the menu planning process undertaken by the catering department they can help to ensure that menus meet the needs of patients. Although the majority of dietitians (83 per cent) were involved in the process, more than a third felt that menu choice at the trust was inadequate. Trusts should ensure that these concerns are adequately taken into account.

11. Each catering department should work from standard costed recipes to ensure consistency of quality and cost, and to aid control of the service. Dietitians should ensure recipes provide sufficient calories and protein. However, only 51 per cent of trusts were using such recipes. In other trusts, menus and standard recipes were generally poorly documented and infrequently used. The implementation of the national standard recipes, with nutritional analysis, should help to bring national standards to all trusts in England.[I] In Wales, hospital nutrition teams will report on the adequacy of patients' meals and quality of services to a named trust board member and each trust will establish a nutrition study to develop policy and practice.[II]

12. A patient's nutritional needs can only be met if he or she eats the meal. It is therefore very important that food as well as being nutritious, is high quality, appetising and served to patients with staff encouragement and assistance if needed.

I Further details can be found in the National Dish Selector on the web site www.betterhospitalfood.com

II National Assembly for Wales. January 2001. *Improving Health in Wales*.

Quality

13. The quality of the service provided can be considered in terms of:

- patient satisfaction;
- relationship to cost; and
- presentation and delivery of the meal service.

Patient satisfaction

14. In 1996 the Department of Health set national standards for catering.[1] These included a questionnaire for trusts to measure patient satisfaction and set the following performance targets:

- Seventy per cent or more patients should give the service seven or more out of ten.
- No more than ten per cent should give the service five or less out of ten.

15. The Audit Commission survey asked trusts to report patient satisfaction against these targets. The average score on food quality and meal service was 7.6. This is a positive endorsement of hospital food and the Commission's auditors have found many examples of high quality meals for example meals cooked to order, ethnic meals produced on site and appetising puréed foods.

16. However, more than a third of trusts do not meet these Department of Health targets [EXHIBIT 1]. Auditors will be helping trusts in the lower quartile of the distribution to investigate why patients are not satisfied and how the service can be improved.

EXHIBIT 1

Percentage of patients who gave the service 7 or more out of 10

There is wide variation between trusts.

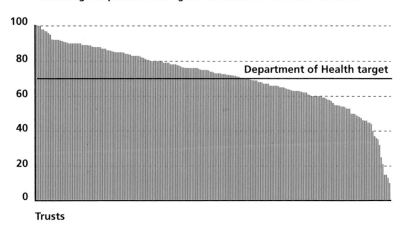

Percentage of patients who gave the service 7 or more out of 10

Department of Health target

Trusts

Source: Audit Commission

1   Department of Health. 1996. *Hospital Catering – Delivering a Quality Service.*

17. These are overall satisfaction levels and reflect a variety of aspects of the catering service including the extent of choice, whether meals are appetising, and how they are served. Trusts use various methods for cooking and service [Boxes B and C] but there was no relationship between the type of method used and overall patient satisfaction.

Box B

Percentage of trusts using the different production methods

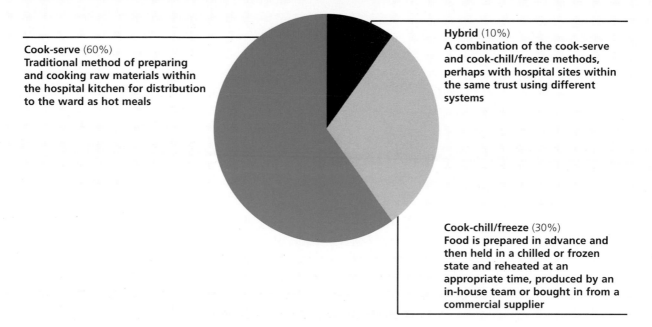

Cook-serve (60%)
Traditional method of preparing and cooking raw materials within the hospital kitchen for distribution to the ward as hot meals

Hybrid (10%)
A combination of the cook-serve and cook-chill/freeze methods, perhaps with hospital sites within the same trust using different systems

Cook-chill/freeze (30%)
Food is prepared in advance and then held in a chilled or frozen state and reheated at an appropriate time, produced by an in-house team or bought in from a commercial supplier

Box C

Percentage of trusts using the different methods of meal service

Bulk service (37%)
Food is placed in bulk in large containers or trays and served on the ward from a trolley by either catering or ward staff. There is some flexibility in portion size using this method

Hybrid (28%)
A combination of the two service methods, perhaps with some wards using a plated system and some having a bulk service

Plated service (35%)
Food is individually plated either within the hospital kitchen or as bought-in cook-chill/freeze meals. They are then delivered in a trolley to the wards and usually served by a member of ward staff

18. NHS Estates is currently reviewing the national questionnaire as part of its responsibility of overseeing the implementation of 'Better Hospital Food'. The questionnaire would benefit from a simplified scoring system and more factual questions that determine the level of service received. In England, patient satisfaction, along with other quality measures of the implementation of the NHS Plan such as the provision of a 24-hour meal service, will form part of the Performance Assessment Framework relating to catering. A more reliable system of quality measurement will enable more meaningful comparisons between trusts. In Wales, patient satisfaction surveys that include questions on hospital food must be provided to trust boards so that they can regularly evaluate the quality and standard of their catering services.[1]

Patient satisfaction shows no relationship to the cost of providing a catering service.

Relationship between quality and costs

19. Patient satisfaction (as currently measured) shows no relationship to the cost of providing a catering service (measured per patient day to take account of differences in the size of departments). This is true whether costs are measured as net expenditure (offsetting income against gross costs) or as gross cost.

20. A possible reason for this is that costs relate solely to the catering department whereas there are many stages and staff involved in delivering a catering service that could affect the patient satisfaction score [BOX D].

---

1   National Assembly for Wales. January 2001. *Improving Health in Wales.*

Box D

There are many stages and staff involved in delivering hospital catering services

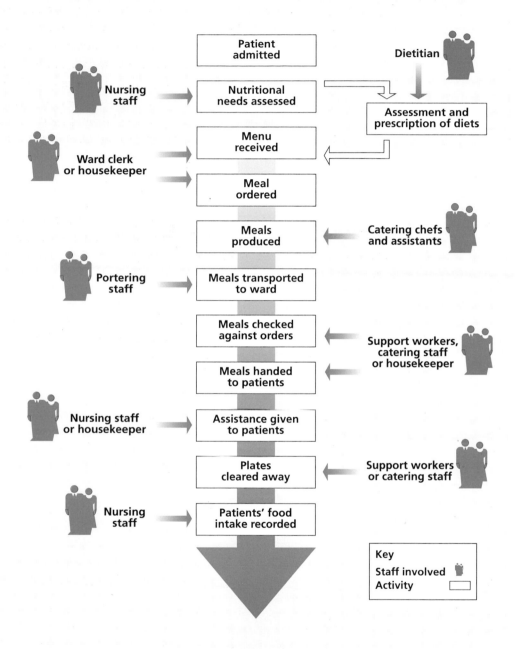

Key
Staff involved
Activity

Presentation and delivery of the meal service

21. Meals may be the highest quality but the value is lost unless the patient actually consumes them. Presentation and delivery can have a big impact [BOX E].

Box E

Quality of meal service

These are the most common examples of a poor quality of service, gathered by auditors.

- Hot food is served cold because the doors to the trolley have remained open whilst one member of staff struggles to hand out meals over 15 minutes.

- Patients do not always receive the meal they ordered either because they are at the end of the ward and their meal has been given to another patient or they have just been admitted and get the meal ordered by the previous bed occupant.

- Patients are often unable to eat their meals because they cannot reach them, have not been given the appropriate cutlery or they need help with awkward lids or wrappers.

- Elderly patients are not always given the assistance they need to feed themselves and in many hospitals no one checks how much they have eaten.

- Maternity patients often miss the set meal times and may go without food for long periods.

- Meal times are not always respected as the major part of a patient's day. They are often disturbed by doctors carrying out ward rounds and nurses undertaking routine observations.

22. It is essential that all staff involved in the 'catering chain' work together as a team to overcome problems such as those detailed in Box E. This includes catering staff, nurses, support workers, housekeepers and dietitians. Roles and responsibilities must be clear and staff need to work within agreed protocols and be fully trained. In England the NHS Plan advocates establishing ward housekeepers who take overall responsibility for the quality and quantity of food served on the wards.[I] Trusts will now have a plan for introducing ward housekeepers so that by 2004, 50 per cent of trusts will have them in place. The introduction of ward housekeepers provides an ideal opportunity for trusts to review the present roles and responsibilities of staff groups in relation to catering and identify how these could be reconfigured to improve the service.

23. Three-quarters of trusts surveyed by the Audit Commission have identified the need to improve the service of meals and the assessment and review of nutrition, and have conducted audits in these areas over the past two years. In 2000 the Department of Health issued the 'Essence of Care' toolkit that contained patient-focused benchmarks for food and nutrition.[II] This tool kit is designed to bring together staff in all disciplines to identify how the service to the patient can be improved.

I   Department of Health. July 2000. *NHS Plan*. Further details can be found on the web site www.betterhospitalfood.com

II   Department of Health. 2000. *Essence of Care*.

24. However, trusts must consider cost as well as quality. They must review the cost in terms of how efficiently and effectively resources are used, otherwise simply increasing spending on catering is unlikely to be the most economic use of trusts' resources.

Expenditure on catering services

25. The components of catering department costs are food and beverages, staff, consumables and overheads [EXHIBIT 2].

EXHIBIT 2

Breakdown of total costs for a typical trust

Typically food and beverages and staff account for 90 per cent of the total cost.

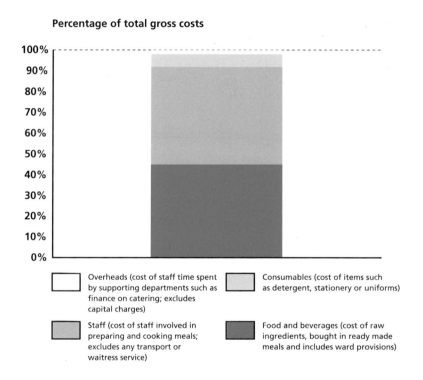

Percentage of total gross costs

Overheads (cost of staff time spent by supporting departments such as finance on catering; excludes capital charges)

Staff (cost of staff involved in preparing and cooking meals; excludes any transport or waitress service)

Consumables (cost of items such as detergent, stationery or uniforms)

Food and beverages (cost of raw ingredients, bought in ready made meals and includes ward provisions)

Source: Audit Commission

26. Trusts will receive income from providing non-patient services (see Box A on page 1) such as the staff restaurant, meals served in the post graduate centre or from providing a meals-on-wheels service for a local authority. In most trusts this income is retained within the catering department to offset the gross costs of providing patient and non-patient services. In effect this means that trusts reduce the total catering budget by the predicted income, releasing the money for use in other areas of the hospital. Comparisons of catering expenditure given below [EXHIBIT 3, overleaf] are therefore based on net expenditure.

EXHIBIT 3

Net expenditure per patient day

The cost of providing catering services varies widely between trusts.

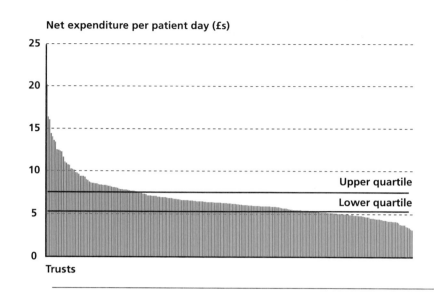

Source: Audit Commission

27. There is wide variation in the net expenditure per patient day, ranging from £2.80 to £20.00. Some of this will be due to the level of income generated from non-patient services and the trust's pricing policies. This issue is considered later. Some of the variation is explained by economies of scale: larger trusts usually have lower average costs [TABLE 1].[1]

---

[1] Using a multiple regression model incorporating size, cooking method and service provider, the only factor to be significant in explaining some of the variation in cost was size.

TABLE 1

Total net expenditure per patient day by different types of trust

The cost of the catering department will depend on the size, location and type of trust.

Trust type	Total net expenditure per patient day
Outside London (non-specialist) trusts	
Small	**£6.56**
Medium	**£5.91**
Large	**£5.46**
London trusts	**£7.64**
Specialist trusts	**£7.70**

Source: Audit Commission

There is no association between the net cost of catering and whether the service is provided externally or in-house...

28. The location and type of trust also affects costs. Trusts based in London and specialist trusts (children's, orthopaedic, women's, cancer and eye hospitals) are more than 20 per cent more expensive than non-specialist trusts outside London [TABLE 1]. For trusts based in London this is due to higher staff salaries and greater food and beverages cost (35 per cent more than the average).

29. There is no association between the net cost of catering and whether the service is provided externally or in-house, or with the type of cooking method used (see Boxes B and C on page 5).[I]

Control of costs

30. Patient and non-patient services need to be considered separately.

Patient services

31. The essence of cost control is to establish the cost of ingredients for particular meals and then the average daily cost for food and beverage for each patient. The Department of Health's 'Delivering a Quality Service' recommends that trusts set a daily food allowance and monitor whether they spend the full allowance and hence whether patients are receiving value for money from the service.[II] Three-quarters of trusts have made a conscious decision on their level of spending on patient food and beverages by setting a daily food budget per patient day. However, only 66 per cent of all trusts monitor the actual costs to check that patients receive the full allowance.

32. When reviewing spending on food and beverages, a trust must be compared with those using a similar method of production. For example, the food costs of cook-chill/freeze meals bought in from a commercial supplier are higher as they already include an element of labour.

I   Using a multiple regression model incorporating size, cooking method and service provider, the only factor to be significant in explaining some of the variation in cost was size.

II   Department of Health. 1996. *Hospital Catering – Delivering a Quality Service.*

33. The average spending on food and beverages per patient is:

- £2.20 for a cook-serve production system;
- £3.70 for cook-chill/freeze meals bought from a commercial supplier;
- £2.40 for cook-chill/freeze meals made on site; and
- £2.70 for a hybrid production system.

However, there is considerable variation within each method of production. For example, for trusts using a cook-serve production method the range is from £1.24 to £5.88 [EXHIBIT 4].

EXHIBIT 4

Cost of food and beverages per patient day

There is variation in the spending levels between trusts.

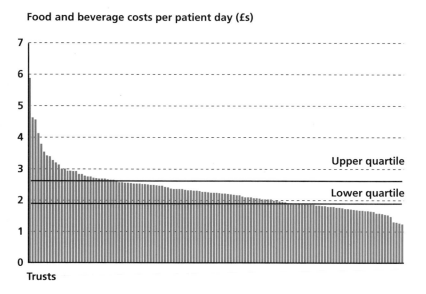

Food and beverage costs per patient day (£s)

Trusts

Source: Audit Commission

34. Variations in food costs do not necessarily mean better or worse ingredients. They may be due to differences in the effectiveness of purchasing or the control of raw ingredients in the production process. So it could be that some trusts in the lower quartile provide the same range and quality of meals as trusts in the upper quartile but at a lower cost. The challenge for trusts will be to meet the NHS Plan requirements of providing a 24-hour service with a ward kitchen service and snack boxes within the current budget.

35. It is likely that some trusts' spending on patient food and beverages will need to increase, particularly those that do not currently offer the recommended choice such as hot meals at night, and those that do not use the high quality fresh ingredients advocated.

Non-patient costs

36. All trusts provide some meals for people other than patients for example staff and visitors. The income generated is retained within the catering department to offset the cost of the service, as previously explained (paragraph 26). This provides an incentive to catering staff to improve performance and offer a high quality service.

37. However, this income does not always cover the cost of providing non-patient services. At present about three-quarters of trusts subsidise their non-patient services [EXHIBIT 5]. Whether non-patient services should make a contribution or be subsidised by the trust must be decided by the trust board, bearing in mind the trust's overall priorities. Almost a fifth of trusts could not provide separate cost information for the different non-patient activities.

EXHIBIT 5

Contribution/subsidy level of non-patient services

Three-quarters of trusts currently subsidise their non-patient services.

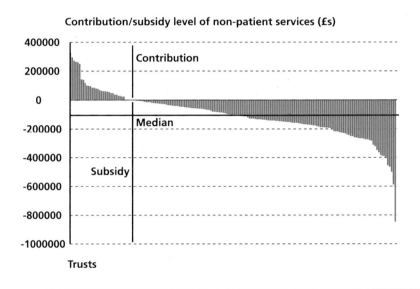

Contribution/subsidy level of non-patient services (£s)

Source: Audit Commission

38. Only 35 per cent of trusts in the Audit Commission survey monitor the actual contribution or subsidy achieved from providing non-patient services. Even fewer have established an appropriate level of subsidy and set a target. The average subsidy is approximately £153,000 per annum; this is equivalent to an additional 84 pence that could be spent daily on food and beverages for each patient. The correct pricing structure depends on the priorities of the trust, so it is important that trusts have the information to set appropriate pricing policies for each non-patient service.

39. There are numerous reasons why one trust may have a higher level of subsidy then another including:

- Longer opening hours in the staff restaurant, perhaps with a night service available for junior doctors to meet New Deal requirements.

- Discounts offered to staff to ease recruitment and retention problems.

- Poor location of the staff restaurant or the facilities available to full-paying customers such as visitors.

40. The staff/visitor restaurant at a trust accounts on average for 69 per cent of non-patient expenditure. In 1967 the Ancillary Staff Council established a pricing policy for staff meals, stating that the cost of food and beverages should account for 60 per cent of the selling price.[1] This directive still seems to be influencing pricing policy, as surprisingly the median distribution of food and beverage costs is nearing 60 per cent of income [EXHIBIT 6]. However, clearly some trusts have moved away from this policy and have begun to set prices based on local subsidy decisions.

EXHIBIT 6

Cost of food and beverages for non-patient services as a proportion of income received

Food and beverage costs as a percentage of income varies between trusts but a third of trusts lie in the range between 55 per cent and 65 per cent.

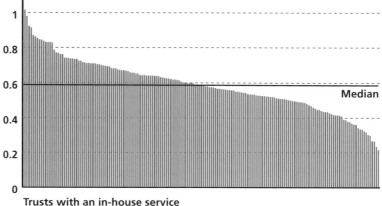

Non-patient food costs as a proportion of income

Median

Trusts with an in-house service

Source: Audit Commission

41. Only a third of trusts have a computerised catering information system to help them set appropriate prices and monitor costs of catering activities. Many are not using these systems to their full potential, often because there has been insufficient investment in staff time to maintain the information.

42. Trusts need integrated systems for planning, procurement and production based on historical information, and for routinely monitoring cost, volumes and wastage. These systems are likely to consider the catering department as one operation. The information needed for making decisions on subsidy levels for each non-patient activity could therefore be the result of a one-off audit that captures cost and income, rather than a continual apportionment of costs. However, it is important that all trusts can provide assurance that funds allocated for feeding patients are not being re-directed into subsidising non-patient services.

I   Department of Health. 1967. *Ancillary Staff Council Meals* (HM67/10). This also states that one meal per day (ASC meal) should be available to staff where food and beverage costs should account for 75 per cent of the selling price.

Food wastage

43. The levels of food wastage not only impact on the cost of a catering service, they also reflect the quality of the service provided. Auditors carried out an independent survey of six wards in each trust. The survey reviewed only 'unserved meals' because of the practical difficulties in measuring wastage left on the plate after patients have eaten (plate waste).

44. The auditors' survey found that wastage rates vary by the type of service method used [**EXHIBIT 7**] (see Box C on page 5 for an explanation of the different service delivery methods). Trusts using the bulk service method experience considerably higher wastage rates because food is served in trays of a set size and if the tray contains eight portions then eight portions are produced even though only (say) six have been ordered. This problem has been overcome in some trusts by using different sizes of trays.

EXHIBIT 7

Percentage food wastage (unserved meals) by service delivery method

More than three-quarters of trusts waste over 10 per cent of the meals produced.

Source: Audit Commission

Percentage meals (unserved) wasted on wards

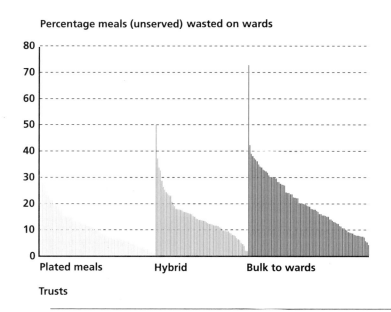

45. It is undesirable to draw conclusions about the most effective delivery method based on the food wastage results alone: the quality and cost of the service offered must also be considered. However, it is important to remember that there is so far no demonstrable relationship between the method of service delivery and patient satisfaction, as currently measured (paragraph 17). Improvement in the validity of patient satisfaction measurement and the adoption of further quality measures, as discussed earlier, should provide future evidence on the impact that the production or service method has on patients and on costs.

46. The annual cost to the NHS of food wasted from 'unserved meals' is £18 million, or an average of £55,000 per trust. This can often be reduced and controlled through improving communication between the catering department and the wards. Some trusts operate a system of confirming the number of meals required just a couple of hours before they are due to be served. It is difficult and counterproductive to reduce wastage to zero as this could have an adverse effect on the quality of service provided, by reducing flexibility of meal choice and portion size. However, if all hospitals achieved the lower quartile level for trusts of their type, this would save the NHS a total of £8 million, or the equivalent of an additional 25 pence that could be spent on food for patients each day.

47. The main reasons for unserved meals are either that the catering department issues more meals than are requested or the wards order more meals than there are patients. Additional meals may be ordered for newly admitted patients but meals are often not cancelled for patients who have been discharged, are in the operating theatre or are 'nil by mouth'. Trusts should have a system in place for adjusting the number of meals ordered by cancelling those not required and being flexible enough to provide additional meals at short notice.